The Chord Songbook
metallica

Wise Publications
London/New York/Paris/Sydney/Copenhagen/Madrid

Exclusive Distributors:
Music Sales Limited
8/9 Frith Street,
London W1V 5TZ, England.
Music Sales Pty Limited
120 Rothschild Avenue,
Rosebery, NSW 2018, Australia.

Order No. AM944680
ISBN 0-7119-6658-3
This book © Copyright 1997 by Wise Publications

Compiled by Peter Evans
Edited by Arthur Dick
Music arranged by Dave Holmes
Music processed by The Pitts

Cover design by Pearce Marchbank, Studio Twenty
Cover photograph by London Features International

Printed in the United Kingdom by
Caligraving Limited, Thetford, Nolfolk.

Your Guarantee of Quality
As publishers, we strive to produce every book
to the highest commercial standards.
This book has been carefully designed to minimise awkward
page turns and to make playing from it a real pleasure.
Particular care has been given to specifying acid-free,
neutral-sized paper made from pulps which have not been
elemental chlorine bleached. This pulp is from farmed sustainable
forests and was produced with special regard for the environment.
Throughout, the printing and binding have been planned to
ensure a sturdy, attractive publication which should give years
of enjoyment. If your copy fails to meet our high standards,
please inform us and we will gladly replace it.

Music Sales' complete catalogue describes thousands
of titles and is available in full colour sections by subject,
direct from Music Sales Limited. Please state your areas of interest
and send a cheque/postal order for £1.50 for postage to:
Music Sales Limited, Newmarket Road,
Bury St. Edmunds, Suffolk IP33 3YB.

Visit the Internet Music Shop at
http://www.musicsales.co.uk

Relative Tuning

The guitar can be tuned with the aid of pitch pipes or dedicated electronic guitar tuners which are available through your local music dealer. If you do not have a tuning device, you can use relative tuning. Estimate the pitch of the 6th string as near as possible to E or at least a comfortable pitch (not too high, as you might break other strings in tuning up). Then, while checking the various positions on the diagram, place a finger from your left hand on the:

5th fret of the E or 6th string and **tune the open A**(or 5th string) to the note (A)

5th fret of the A or 5th string and **tune the open D** (or 4th string) to the note (D)

5th fret of the D or 4th string and **tune the open G** (or 3rd string) to the note (G)

4th fret of the G or 3rd string and **tune the open B** (or 2nd string) to the note (B)

5th fret of the B or 2nd string and **tune the open E** (or 1st string) to the note (E)

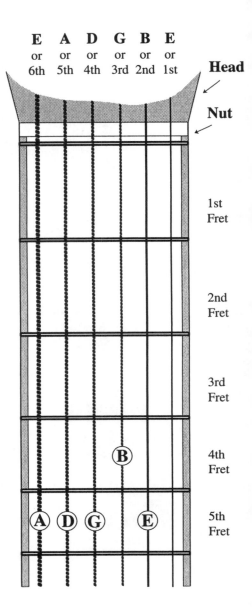

Reading Chord Boxes

Chord boxes are diagrams of the guitar neck viewed head upwards, face on as illustrated. The top horizontal line is the nut, unless a higher fret number is indicated, the others are the frets.

The vertical lines are the strings, starting from E (or 6th) on the left to E (or 1st) on the right.

The black dots indicate where to place your fingers.

Strings marked with an O are played open, not fretted.

Strings marked with an X should not be played.

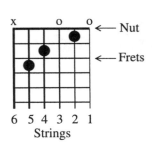

4

Ain't My Bitch

Words & Music by
James Hetfield & Lars Ulrich

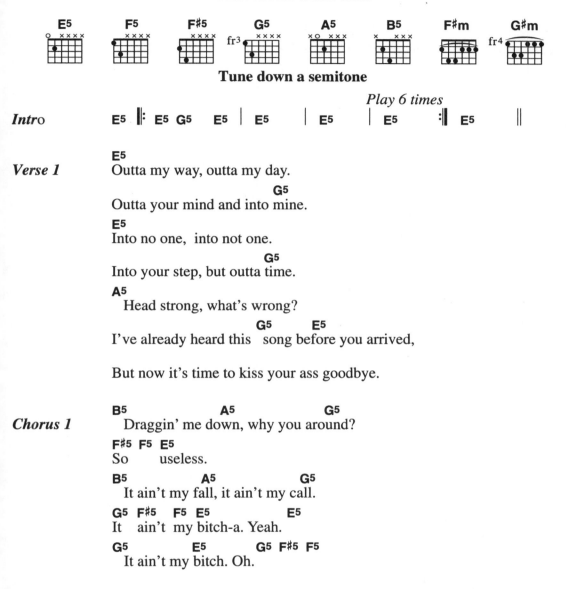

Tune down a semitone

Intro

Verse 1

E5
Outta my way, outta my day.

G5
Outta your mind and into mine.

E5
Into no one, into not one.

G5
Into your step, but outta time.

A5
Head strong, what's wrong?

G5   **E5**
I've already heard this   song before you arrived,

But now it's time to kiss your ass goodbye.

Chorus 1

B5   **A5**   **G5**
Draggin' me down, why you around?

F♯5 F5 E5
So   useless.

B5   **A5**   **G5**
It ain't my fall, it ain't my call.

G5 F♯5 F5 E5   **E5**
It   ain't my bitch-a. Yeah.

G5   **E5**   **G5 F♯5 F5**
It ain't my bitch. Oh.

Verse 2

E5
Down on the sun, down and no fun.

                                G5
Down and out, where the hell ya been?

E5
Damn it on down, damn it unbound.

                            G5
Damn it all down to hell again.

A5
  Stand tall, can't fall.

                        G5   **E5**
Never even bend at all before you arrived,

But now it's time to kiss your ass goodbye.

Chorus 2

B5   **A5**   **G5**
  Draggin' me down, why you around?

F♯5 F5 E5
So   useless.

B5   **A5**   **G5**
  It ain't my fall, it ain't my call.

G5 F♯5   F5 E5
It   ain't my bitch-a.

| **E5** | **E5** | **E5** | **E5 G5   E5** |

‖: **E5** | **E5**   :‖   *Play 7 times*

Yo, outta my way

Solo

‖: **F♯m** | **F♯m** | **F♯m** | **A5** :‖

‖: **G♯m** | **G♯m** | **G♯m** | **B5** :‖

‖: **E5** | **E5** | **E5** | **E5** :‖

Verse 3

As Verse 1

G5   **F♯5**
  (And now it's time to kiss your ass   goodbye)

              F5
(And now it's time to kiss you.)

Chorus 3

B5   A5   G5
Draggin' me down, why you around?

F#5 F5 E5
So   useless, yeah.

B5   A5   G5
It ain't my fall, it ain't my call.

G5 F#5   F5   E5
It ain't my bitch, oh.

B5   A5   G5
No way but down, why you around?

F#5 F5 E5
No   foolin' yeah.

B5   A5   G5
It ain't my smile, it ain't my style.

G5 F#5   F5   E5
It ain't my bitch, no it ain't mine.

Outro

B5   A5
Ain't mine, your kind,

G5   E5
You're steppin' outta time.

B5   A5
Ain't mine, your kind,

G5   E5
You're steppin' outta time.

B5   A5
Draggin' me down, why you around?

G5 E5
No foolin'.

B5   A5   G5
It ain't my fall, it ain't my call,

   F#5   F5   E5
It ain't my ooh, bitch.

You ain't mine.

Coda

| E5 | E5 | E5 | E5   ‖

Bleeding Me

Words & Music by
James Hetfield, Lars Ulrich & Kirk Hammett

Em   D   Dsus4   G5   A5   B5   C5   D5   E5

Tune down a semitone

Intro ‖: Em | Em | Em | Em :‖   *Play 6 times*

Verse 1

Em
I'm digging my way,

I'm digging my way to somethin',

I'm digging my way to somethin' better.

I'm pushin' to stay,

I'm pushin' to stay with somethin',

I'm pushin' to stay with somethin' better.
(Em) | D Dsus4 D | D Dsus4 D | Em |
Woh.
(Em) | D Dsus4 D | D Dsus4 D | A5   G5 |
Woh.

‖: Em | Em | Em | Em :‖

Verse 2

Em
I'm sowin' the seeds,

I'm sowin' the seeds I've taken,

I'm sowin' the seeds I take for granted.

This thorn in my side,

This thorn in my side is from the tree,

This thorn in my side is from the tree I've planted.

cont.

(Em) | **D Dsus⁴ D** | **D Dsus⁴ D** | **Em** |
Oh it tears me and I bleed, yeah.

(Em) | **D Dsus⁴ D** | **D Dsus⁴ D** | **A⁵**   **G⁵** |
And I bleed, yeah, yeah.

Chorus 1

E⁵   **D⁵**
Caught under wheel's roll,

         A⁵
I take the leech, I'm bleeding me.

E⁵   **D⁵**
  Can't stop to save my soul,

         A⁵
I take the leash that's leading me.

E⁵   **D⁵**
  I'm bleeding me.

D⁵   **A⁵**
  Woh, ooh, I can't take it.

E⁵   **D⁵**
  Caught under wheel's roll.

A⁵   **Em**   **D Dsus⁴ D** | **D Dsus⁴ D** | **Em** |
Oh, the bleeding of me,   yeah.

        Em   **D Dsus⁴ D** | **D Dsus⁴ D** |
Ooh, of me,   yeah.

A⁵   **G⁵ Em**
  The bleeding of   me.

Interlude 1   ‖: **(Em)** | **Em** | **Em** | **Em**   :‖   *Play 4 times*

Chorus 2

E⁵   **D⁵**
Caught under wheel's roll,

         A⁵
I take the leech, I'm bleeding me.

E⁵   **D⁵**
  Can't stop to save my soul,

         A⁵
I take the leash that's leading me.

E⁵   **D⁵**
  I'm bleeding me.

cont.

    (D5)   **A5**
    Woh, ooh, I can't take it.
    E5   **D5**
    Caught under wheel's roll.
    A5   **Em**
Oh, the bleeding of me,

Oh, the bleeding of me.

Interlude 2   ‖: **E5** | **E5** | **E5** | **E5**   :‖   *Play 4 times*

Bridge

    E5
    I am the beast that feeds the beast,

I am the blood, I am release.

Come make me pure, bleed me a cure.

I'm caught, I'm caught, I'm caught under.

Chorus 3

    E5   **D5**
Caught under wheel's roll,
          A5
I take the leech, I'm bleeding me.
E5   **D5**
    Can't stop to save my soul,
          A5
I take the leash that's leading me.
E5   **D5**
    I'm bleeding me.
A5
Oh, I can't take it.
E5   **D5**
    I can't take it, I can't take it.
       A5   **E5**
Oh, oh the bleeding of me.

Solo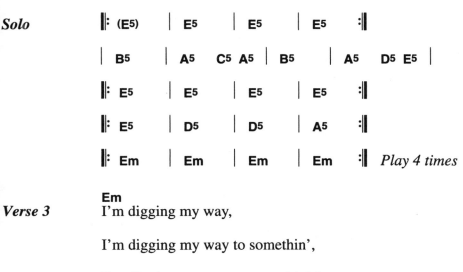

Verse 3

Em
I'm digging my way,

I'm digging my way to somethin',

I'm digging my way to somethin' better.

I'm pushin' to stay,

I'm pushin' to stay with somethin',

I'm pushin' to stay with somethin' better,

With somethin' better.

Enter Sandman

Words & Music by
James Hetfield, Lars Ulrich & Kirk Hammett

E5   A5   G5 fr3   F#5   F5   B5

Intro

‖: E5 A5 | E5 A5 | E5 A5 | E5 A5 :‖   *Play 3 times*

‖: E5 | E5 | E5 | E5 :‖   *Play 4 times*

‖: E5 A5 | E5 A5 | E5 A5 | G5 F#5 E5 :‖

Verse 1

E5   F5 E5
Say your prayers, little one,

E5   F5 E5   G5   F#5 G5 F#5 E5
Don't forget my son, to include ev'ry one.

E5   F5 E5
I tuck you in, warm within,

E5   F5 E5   G5   F#5 G5 F#5
Keep you free from sin 'til the sandman he comes,   ah.

Bridge 1

F#5 B5   F#5   B5
Sleep with one eye open,

F#5 B5   F#5   B5
Gripping your pillow tight.

Chorus 1

F#5 B5 F#5 B5 F#5 B5   E5
Ex - it light.   En - ter   night.

F#5 B5 E5   G5   F#5 G5 F#5   E5
Take my hand. We're off to never-ne - ver land.

Instrumental ‖: (E5) A5 | E5 A5 | E5 A5 | E5 F#5 G5 E5 :‖

Verse 2

E5   F5 E5
Something's wrong, shut the light,

E5   F5 E5   G5   F#5 G5 F#5 E5
Heavy thoughts tonight, and they aren't of Snow White.

E5   F5 E5
Dreams of war dreams of liars,

(E5)   F5 E5   G5   F#5 G5 F#5
Dreams of dragons fire   and of things that will bite,   yeah.

Bridge 2   As Bridge 1

Chorus 2   As Chorus 1

Solo   Over Verse 1, Bridge 1 and Chorus 1 ad lib.

Middle
```
E5              A5              E5              A5
```
Now I lay me down to sleep, (now I lay me down to sleep,)
```
E5                  A5              E5                  A5
```
Pray the Lord my soul to keep, (pray the Lord my soul to keep,)
```
E5          A5          E5      A5
```
If I die before I wake, (if I die before I wake,)
```
E5                  A5              E5                  A5
```
Pray the Lord my soul to take, (pray the Lord my soul to take.)
```
F#5         B5      F#5         B5
```
Hush little baby, don't say a word
```
F#5             B5          F#5         B5
```
  And never mind that noise you heard,
```
F#5             B5          F#5         B5
```
  It's just the beasts under your bed,
```
F#5         B5      F#5         B5
```
  In your closet, in your head.

Chorus 3
```
F#5 B5 F#5   B5 F#5 B5   E5
```
Ex - it   light.   En - ter   night.
```
F#5             E5
```
Grain of sand.
```
F#5 B5 F#5   B5 F#5 B5   E5
```
Ex - it   light.   En - ter   night.
```
F#5     B5  E5              G5      F#5     G5 F#5  E5
```
Take   my hand, we're off to never-ne-ver-land,   yeah.

Outro
```
│ E5  A5 │ E5  A5 │ E5  A5 │ E5  A5 │

│ E5  A5 │ E5  A5 │ E5  A5 │ E5  F#5  G5  E5 │

‖: E5  A5 │ E5  A5 │ E5  A5 │ E5  A5 :‖   Repeat to fade
```

13

Fade To Black

Words & Music by
James Hetfield, Lars Ulrich, Cliff Burton & Kirk Hammett

Bm	Bm/A	A/C#	E	F6	Am	C	G

Em	Eaug	A5	C5	D5	E5	G5	F#5	B5

Intro   ‖: Bm | Bm/A | Bm | A/C# :‖ *Play 5 times*

| F6 E | E |

‖: Am | C | G | Em :‖ *Play 4 times*

Verse 1

Am   C
Life it seems will fade away,

G   Em
Drifting further ev'ry day.

Am   C
Getting lost within myself,

G   Em
Nothing matters, no-one else.

Am   C
I have lost the will to live,

G   Em
Simply nothing more to give.

Am   C
There is nothing more for me.

G   Eaug
Need the end to set me free.

Interlude 1   ‖: A5 | C5 | A5 D5 | E5 |

| A5 | C5 | A5 G5 F#5 | E5 :‖

Interlude 2   ‖: Am | C | G | Em :‖

Verse 2

Am   C
Things not what they used to be,
G   Em
Missing one inside of me.
Am   C
Deathly lost, this can't be real,
G   Em
Cannot stand this hell I feel.
Am   C
Emptiness is filling me
G   Em
To the point of agony.
Am   C
Growing darkness taking dawn,
G   Eaug
I was me but now he's gone.

Interlude 3   As Interlude 1

Interlude 4   ‖: D5 E5 | D5 E5 G5 F#5 | D5 | D5   :‖

Bridge 1

D5 E5   D5 E5   G5 F#5   D5
No one but me can save myself but it's too late.
D5   E5   D5 E5   G5   F#5 D5
Now I can't think, think why I should even try.

Interlude 5   As Interlude 4

Bridge 2

D5 E5   D5 E5   G5 F#5   D5
Yesterday seems as though it nev-er existed.
D5   E5   D5 E5   G5 F#5   D5
Death greets me warm, now I will just say goodbye.

Interlude 6   ‖: E5 | E5   G5 F#5 | E5   D5 | D5   :‖

Outro solo   ‖: B5 | B5 | A5 | A5 |

               | G5 | G5 | A5 | A5   :‖ *Repeat to fade*

For Whom The Bell Tolls

Words & Music by
James Hetfield, Lars Ulrich & Cliff Burton

E5   G5   C5   A5   B♭5   F#5   F5   B5

Verse 1

E5
Make his fight on the hill on the early day.
G5
Constant chill deep inside.
E5
Shouting gun, on they run through the endless grey.
G5
On they fight for they're right.
C5   A5
Yes, but who's to say?
E5
For a hill men would kill. Why? They do not know.
G5
Suffered wounds test their pride.
E5
Men of five, still alive through the raging glow.
G5
Gone insane from the pain
C5   A5   E5 G5 E5 A5
That they surely know.

Chorus 1

E5 G5   B♭5   F#5   E5 G5 E5 A5
        For whom the bell tolls,
E5 G5 B♭5 F#5   F5 E5 G5 E5 A5
Time marches   on
E5 G5   B♭5   F#5   E5 G5 E5 A5   E5 G5 B♭5 F#5 F5
For whom the bell tolls.

Interlude   ‖: E5 | E5 | E5 | G5 | E5 | B5 :‖

Verse 2

E5
Take a look to the sky just before you die.

G5
It's the last time he will.

E5
Blackened roar, massive roar fills the crumbling sky.

G5
Shattered goal fills his soul

C5   **A5**
With a ruthless cry.

E5
Stranger now are his eyes to this mystery.

G5
Hear the silence so loud.

E5
Crack of dawn, all is gone except the will to be.

G5
Now they see what will be,

C5   **A5**   **E5 G5 E5 A5**
Blinded eyes to see.

Chorus 2

E5 G5   **B♭5**   **F♯5**   **E5 G5 E5 A5**
For whom the bell tolls,

E5 G5 B♭5 **F♯5**   **F5** **E5 G5 E5 A5**
Time marches   on

E5 G5   **B♭5**   **F♯5**   **E5 G5 E5 A5**   **E5 G5 B♭5 F♯5 F5**
For whom the bell tolls.

Coda

‖: E5 F♯5 | E5 F♯5 | G5 :‖ *Repeat to fade*

Hero Of The Day

Words & Music by
James Hetfield, Lars Ulrich & Kirk Hammett

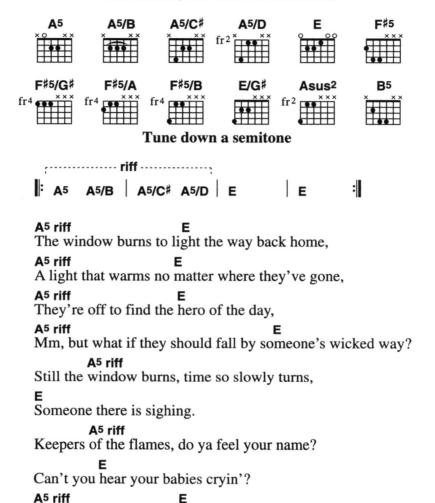

Tune down a semitone

Intro

```
r -------- riff -------- ר
|: A5  A5/B | A5/C#  A5/D | E      | E      :|
```

Verse 1

A5 riff   **E**
The window burns to light the way back home,

A5 riff   **E**
A light that warms no matter where they've gone,

A5 riff   **E**
They're off to find the hero of the day,

A5 riff   **E**
Mm, but what if they should fall by someone's wicked way?

           A5 riff
Still the window burns, time so slowly turns,

E
Someone there is sighing.

           A5 riff
Keepers of the flames, do ya feel your name?

           E
Can't you hear your babies cryin'?

A5 riff   **E**
Mama, they try and break me,

A5 riff   **E**
Still they try and break me.

Verse 2

A⁵ riff   **E**
Excuse me while I tend to how I feel,

A⁵ riff   **E**
These things return to me that still seem real.

A⁵ riff   **E**
Now, deservingly, this easy chair,

A⁵ riff   **E**
Mm, but the rocking stopped by wheels of despair.

      A⁵ riff
Don't want your aid,

                              E
But the fist I've made for years can't hold off fear.

        A⁵ riff
No, I'm not all me,

                        E   **F♯5**
So please excuse me while I tend to how I feel.

        (F♯5)
Chorus 1   But now the dreams and waking screams

That ever last the night.

So build the wall behind it,

Crawl and hide until it's light.

So can you hear your babies cryin' now?

Solo   ‖: A⁵   A⁵/B ∣ A⁵/C♯ A⁵/D ∣ E   ∣ E   :‖

        A⁵ riff
Verse 3   Still the window burns, time so slowly turns

      E
And someone there is sighing.

        A⁵ riff
Keepers of the flames, can't you hear your names?

        E
Can't you hear your babies cryin'?

19

Chorus 2
F#5
But now the dreams and waking screams

That ever last the night.

So build the wall behind it,

Crawl and hide until it's light.

So can you hear your babies cryin' now?

Outro
F#5   F#5/G#
‖:   Mama, they try and break me,
F#5/A#   F#/B
Mama, they try and break me,
F#5   E/G#
Mama, they try and break me,
Asus2   B5   F#5
Mama, they try, Mama they try. :‖

Leper Messiah

Words & Music by
James Hetfield & Lars Ulrich

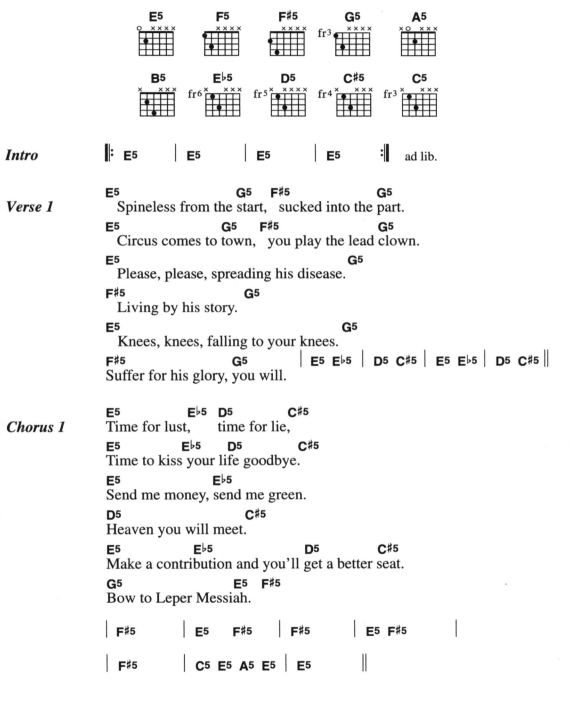

Intro   ‖: E5 | E5 | E5 | E5 :‖ ad lib.

Verse 1

E5   G5   F#5   G5
   Spineless from the start,   sucked into the part.

E5   G5   F#5   G5
   Circus comes to town,   you play the lead clown.

E5   G5
   Please, please, spreading his disease.

F#5   G5
   Living by his story.

E5   G5
   Knees, knees, falling to your knees.

F#5   G5 | E5 E♭5 | D5 C#5 | E5 E♭5 | D5 C#5 ‖
Suffer for his glory, you will.

Chorus 1

E5   E♭5 D5   C#5
Time for lust,   time for lie,

E5   E♭5 D5   C#5
Time to kiss your life goodbye.

E5   E♭5
Send me money, send me green.

D5   C#5
Heaven you will meet.

E5   E♭5   D5   C#5
Make a contribution and you'll get a better seat.

G5   E5 F#5
Bow to Leper Messiah.

| F#5 | E5   F#5 | F#5 | E5   F#5 | |

| F#5 | C5   E5   A5   E5 | E5   ‖

Verse 2

E5   G5   F#5   G5
Marvel at his tricks,   need your Sunday fix.

E5   G5   F#5   G5
Blind devotion came,   rotating your brain.

E5   G5
Chain, chain, join the endless chain.

F#5   G5
Taken by his glamour.

E5   G5
Fame, fame, infection is the game.

F#5   G5 | E5 Eb5 | D5 C#5 | E5 Eb5 | D5 C#5 ‖
Stinking drunk with power, we see.

Chorus 2

E5   Eb5   D5   C#5
Time for lust,   time for lie,

E5   Eb5   D5   C#5
Time to kiss your life goodbye.

E5   Eb5
Send me money, send me green.

D5   C#5
Heaven you will meet.

E5   Eb5   D5   C#5
Make a contribution and you'll get a better seat.

G5   E5 F#5
Bow to Leper Messiah.

| F#5 | E5 F#5 | F#5 | E5 F#5 | |
| F#5 | C5 E5 A5 E5 | E5 | E5 | E5 ‖

Interlude 1 ‖: E5 | E5 | F5 | G5 A5 |

| E5 | E5 | D5 | A5 B5 :‖ *Play 3 times*

Bridge

E5
Witchery, weakening,

F5   G5 A5
Sees the sheep are gathering.

E5
Set the trap, hypnotize.

D5   A5 B5
Now you follow.

22

Solo   ‖: E5 | E5 | F5 | G5 A5 |

| E5 | E5 | D5 | A5 B5 :‖

Interlude 2   ‖: E5 | E5 | F5 | G5 A5 |

| E5 | E5 | D5 | A5 B5 :‖

| A5 | A5 | G5 | F♯5 F5 ‖

Chorus 3

E5   E♭5 D5   C♯5
Time for lust,   time for lie,

E5   E♭5 D5   C♯5 E5
Time to kiss your life goodbye.

                E♭5
Send me money, send me green.

D5   C♯5
Heaven you will meet.

E5   E♭5   D5   C♯5 G5
Make a contribution and you'll get a better seat.

E5 E♭5 D5 C♯5
Lie, lie, lie, lie,

E5 E♭5 D5 C♯5
Lie, lie, lie, lie.

Link   ‖: G5 | G5 | G5 | G5 :‖

Outro | E5 | E5 F♯5 | F♯5 | E5 F♯5 |

| F♯5 | E5 F♯5 | F♯5 | C5 E5 A5 E5 |

| E5 | E5 | F5 E5 ‖

23

Mama Said

Words & Music by
James Hetfield & Lars Ulrich

Dm **Dsus4** **C** **Am** **Asus4** **Cadd9** **G** **B♭** **F**

Tune down a semitone

Intro

| Dm Dsus4 Dm | C Am | Dm Dsus4 Dm | C Am ‖

Verse 1

Dm   Dsus4 Dm
Mama, she has taught me well,

C   Am
Told me when I was young,

Dm   Dsus4 Dm
"Son, your life's an open   book,

          C   Am   Asus4
Don't close it 'fore it's done."

          Dm   Dsus4 Dm
The brightest flame burns quickest,

          C   Am   Asus4
That's what I heard her say,

     Dm   Dsus4 Dm
A son's heart's owed to mother

          C   Am
But I must find my way.

Chorus 1

Dm Cadd9 Am   G
Let   my   heart go,

Dm Cadd9 Am   G
Let   your son grow.

          Dm Cadd9 Am   G
Mama, let   my   heart go,

     Dm Cadd9 B♭   G   Am
Or let   this   heart be still, yeah, still.

| Dm Dsus4 Dm | C Am | Dm Dsus4 Dm | C Am ‖

Verse 2

Dm   Dsus4 Dm
"Rebel", my new last name,

C   Am
Wild blood in my veins.

Dm   Dsus4   Dm
Apron strings around my neck,

C   Am
The mark that still remains.

Dm   Dsus4   Dm
I left home at an early age,

C   Am
Of what I heard was wrong.

Dm   Dsus4 Dm
I never asked forgiveness

C   Am
But what I said is done.

Chorus 2

Dm Cadd9 Am   G
Let   my   heart go,

Dm Cadd9 Am   G
Let   your   son grow.

Dm Cadd9 Am   G
Mama, let   my   heart go,

Dm Cadd9 Bb   G   Am   Asus4
Or let   this   heart be still.

Bridge 1

Dm   G   Cadd9 F
Never I ask of you but never I gave,

Dm   G   Cadd9   F
But you gave me your emptiness I now take to my grave.

Dm   G   Cadd9 F
Never I ask of you but never I gave,

Dm   G   Cadd9   F
But you gave me your emptiness I now take to my grave,

Dm Cadd9 Bb   G   Am   Asus4
So let   this   heart be still.

Verse 3

    Dm   **Dsus4 Dm**
Mama, now I'm coming home,

           C   **Am**
I'm not all you wished of me.

    Dm   **Dsus4 Dm**
A mother's love for her son,

         C   **Am**
Unspoken, help me be.

         Dm   **Dsus4 Dm**
Yeah, I took your love for granted,

              C   **Am**
And all the things you said to me, yeah.

    Dm   **Dsus4**   **Dm**
I need your arms to welcome me

         C   **Am**
But a cold stone's all I see.

Chorus 3

                 G
Let my heart go,

Dm   **Cadd9**   **Am**   **G**
Let   your   son grow.

         Dm Cadd9 Am   **G**
Mama, let my   heart go,

      Dm **Cadd9** **B♭**   **G**   **Am**   **Asus4**
Or let   this   heart be still.

Dm **Cadd9** **Am**   **Dm**
Let my   heart go,

        Cadd9 **Am**   **Dm Dsus4 Dm**
Mama, let my   heart go.

               Cadd9 **Am**   **Dm Dsus4 Dm**
Mm, you never let my   heart go.

        Cadd9 **B♭**   **G** **Am**
So let this   heart be still, woh.

| **Dm** **G** | **Cadd9** **F** | **Dm** **G** | **Cadd9** **F** ||

Outro

Dm   **G**   **Cadd9** **F**
Never I ask of you but never I gave,

        Dm   **G**   **Cadd9**   **F**
But you gave me your emptiness I now take to my grave.

Dm   **G**   **Cadd9** **F**
Never I ask of you but never I gave,

        Dm   **G**   **Cadd9**   **F**
But you gave me your emptiness I now take to my grave,

      Dm **Cadd9** **B♭**   **G** **Am**
So let this   heart be still.

Master Of Puppets

Words & Music by
James Hetfield, Lars Ulrich, Cliff Burton & Kirk Hammett

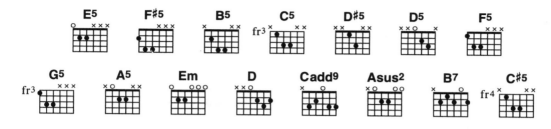

Intro   E5 ad lib.

Verse 1
E5
End of passion play, crumbling away,

I'm your source of self destruction.

Veins that pump with fear, sucking darkest clear,

Leading on your death's construction.
F#5
Taste me you will see, more is all you need,
                                    B5 E5
Dedicated to how I'm killing you.

Pre-chorus 1
B5   C5   D#5 B5   E5   D5 E5
Come crawling   faster,
B5 C5   D#5 B5 E5   D5 E5
   Obey your   master.
B5   C5 D#5 B5 E5   D5 E5
Your life burns faster,
B5   E5   F5
   Obey your master, master.

Chorus 1

E5　　　　　　　　　　　　　　　　　　　**G5**
Master of puppets, I'm pulling your strings,
C5　　　　　　　　　　**B5**　　　　　**A5**
Twisting your mind and smashing your dreams.
D5　　　　　　　　**C5**　　　　**B5**
Blinded by me, you can't see a thing,
E5　　　　　　　　　　　　　　**D5**　　　**C5**
Just call my name 'cause I'll hear you scream.
E5　　**F5**
Master, master.
E5　　　　　　　　　　　　　　　　　　**C5**
Just call my name 'cause I'll hear you scream,
E5　　**F5**
Master, master.

| **E5** | **E5** | **E5** | **E5** |

| **E5** | **E5** | **E5** | **G5** | **G5** ‖

Verse 2

Em
Needle work the way, never you betray,

Life of death becoming clearer.

Pain monopoly, ritual misery,

Chop your breakfast on a mirror.
F♯5
Taste me you will see, more is all you need,
　　　　　　　　　　　　　　　　B5 E5
Dedicated to how I'm killing you.

Pre-chorus 2　　As Pre-chorus 1

Chorus 2　　As Chorus 1

Interlude　‖: **Em** | **D** | **Cadd9** | **Asus2 B7** | **B7** :‖　*Play 4 times*

Solo 1　‖: **Em** | **D** | **Cadd9** | **Asus2 B7** | **B7** :‖　*Play 4 times*

　‖: **E5** | **D5** | **C5** | **A5 B5** | **D♯5** :‖

　| **E5** | **E5** | **F♯5** | **F♯5** | **F♯5** | **F♯5** ‖

Bridge

F#5   G5 C#5
Master, master, where's the dreams that I've been after?

F#5   G5 C#5
Master, master, promised only lies.

F#5   G5 C#5
Laughter, laughter, all I hear or see is laughter,

F#5   G5 C#5
Laughter, laughter, laughing at my cries.

| G5 | G5 | F#5 | F#5 ||

Solo 2

||: E5 | E5 | E5 | E5 :|| *Play 4 times*

||: F#5 | F#5 | F#5 | F#5 :||

| B5 | E5 | Ad lib.

Verse 3

E5
Hell is worth all that, natural habitat,

Just a rhyme without a reason.

Never ending maze, drift on numbered days,

Now your life is out of season.

F#5
I will occupy, I will help you die,

I will run through you,

                     B5 E5
Now I rule you too.

Pre-chorus 3   As Pre-chorus 1

Chorus 3   As Chorus 1

Outro

||: E5 | E5 | E5 | E5 :|| *Play 4 times*

               G5 E5
Ha, Ha, Ha, Ha!

Nothing Else Matters

Words & Music by
James Hetfield & Lars Ulrich

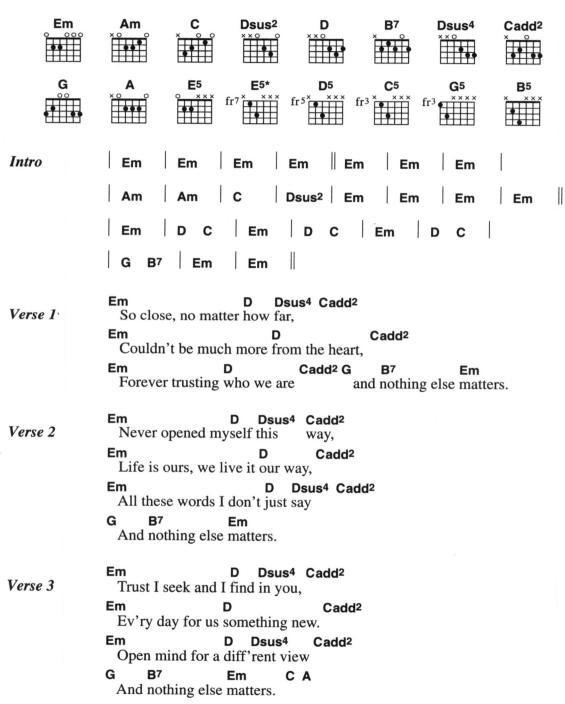

Intro

| Em | Em | Em | Em ‖ Em | Em | Em |

| Am | Am | C | Dsus2 Em | Em | Em | Em ‖

| Em | D C | Em | D C | Em | D C |

| G B7 | Em | Em ‖

Verse 1

Em   D   Dsus4 Cadd2
So close, no matter how far,

Em   D   Cadd2
Couldn't be much more from the heart,

Em   D   Cadd2 G   B7   Em
Forever trusting who we are   and nothing else matters.

Verse 2

Em   D   Dsus4 Cadd2
Never opened myself this   way,

Em   D   Cadd2
Life is ours, we live it our way,

Em   D   Dsus4 Cadd2
All these words I don't just say

G   B7   Em
And nothing else matters.

Verse 3

Em   D   Dsus4 Cadd2
Trust I seek and I find in you,

Em   D   Cadd2
Ev'ry day for us something new.

Em   D   Dsus4   Cadd2
Open mind for a diff'rent view

G   B7   Em   C A
And nothing else matters.

Copyright © 1991 Creeping Death Music, USA.
PolyGram Music Publishing Limited, 47 British Grove, London W4.
All Rights Reserved. International Copyright Secured.

Chorus 1

$$\overset{\text{D}}{}\qquad\qquad\overset{\text{C}}{}\overset{\text{A}}{}$$

    D   C   A
Never cared for what they do,

    D   C   A
Never cared for what they know,

    D   Em
Oh, but I know.

Verse 4   As Verse 1

Chorus 2   As Chorus 1

Instrumental ‖: Em | Em | Am | Am | C | Dadd² | Em | Em :‖

Verse 5   As Verse 2

Verse 6   As Verse 3

Chorus 3

    D   C   A
Never cared for what they say,

    D   C   A
Never cared for games they play,

    D   C   A
Never cared for what they do,

    D   C   A
Never cared for what they know,

    D   Em
Oh and I know, yeah, yeah.

Solo | E⁵ | D⁵ C⁵ | E⁵ | D⁵ C⁵ | E⁵ | D⁵ C⁵ |

         | G⁵ B⁵ | E⁵ | E⁵ | E⁵ | E⁵ ‖

Verse 7

    Em   D   Dsus⁴ Cadd²
So close, no matter how far,

    Em   D   Cadd²
Couldn't be much closer from the heart,

    Em   D   Dsus⁴ Cadd²
Forever trusting who we are.

    G   B⁷   Em
No, nothing else matters.

Outro ‖: Em | Em | Em | Em | Em :‖ *Repeat to fade*

One

Words & Music by
James Hetfield & Lars Ulrich

Bm Gmaj7 D5/A D/A E5 F#5 Em F#m

G5 A5 B5 C#5 D G F C5

Intro   (Bm) Ad lib.

Verse 1
     Bm   **Gmaj7**
     I can't remember anything,
     Bm   **Gmaj7 D5/A**
     Can't tell if this is true or dream.
     Bm   **D/A**
     Deep down inside I feel to scream,
     Gmaj7   **E5 F#5**
     This terrible silence stops me.
     Bm   **Gmaj7**
     Now that the war is through with me,
     Bm   **Gmaj7 D5/A**
     I'm waking up I cannot see
     Bm   **D/A**
     That there's not much left to me.
     Gmaj7   **E5 F#5**
     Nothing is real but pain now!
     G5   A5   B5   A5 G5 F#5 B5   A5 B5 C#5
     Hold my breath as I wish for death,
     B5 A5   **D**
     Oh please God wake me!

Link 1   ‖: (D) | G | F | Em :‖

Verse 2

    Bm   **Gmaj7**
    Back in the womb it's much too real,

    Bm   **Gmaj7 D5/A**
    In pumps life that I must feel,

    Bm   **D/A**
    But I can't look forward to reveal,

    Gmaj7   **E5 F#5**
    Look to the time when I'll live.

    Bm   **Gmaj7**
    Fed through the tube that sticks in me,

    Bm   **Gmaj7 D5/A**
    Just like a wartime novel - ty,

    Bm   **D/A**
    Tied to machines that make me be,

    Gmaj7   **E5**   **F#5**
    Cut this life off from me!

    G5   **A5**   **B5**   **A5 G5 F#5**   **B5**   **A5 B5 C#5**
    Hold my breath as I   wish for death,

    B5 A5   **D**
    Oh please God wake me!

Link 2   ‖: (D) | G | F | Em   :‖   *Play 4 times*

Bridge

    G5   **A5**   **B5**   **A5 G5**
    Now the world is   gone,

    F#5   **B5**   **A5 B5 C#5**
    I'm   just one.

    B5   **A5**   **B5**   **C#5**
    Oh God help me.

    G5   **A5**   **B5**   **A5 G5 F#5**   **B5**   **A5 B5 C#5**
    Hold my breath as I   wish for death,

    B5 A5   **B5**   **C#5 G5**   **A5 B5 A5 G5 F#5 B5**
    Oh please God, help me!

Instrumental   ‖: A5 | G5 | B5 | C5   :‖ *Play 4 times*

                ‖: C5 | D5 | B5 | C5   :‖

                | C5 | C5   ‖ E5 | E5 | E5 |

                | E5 F5 | E5   F5 | E5   F5 | E5   F5 | E5   F5 ‖

Middle

E5
Darkness imprisoning me,

F5
All that I see, absolute horror!

E5
I cannot live! I cannot die!

F5 E5
Trapped in myself, body, my holding cell!

(E5)
Landmine has taken my sight,

F5
Taken my speech, taken my hearing,

E5
Taken my arms, taken my legs,

F5 E5
Taken my soul, left me with life in hell!

Solo   ‖: (E5) | E5   F5 | E5 | E5   F5 | E5 | E5   F5 |

| E5 | E5   F5 | E5 | E5 | E5 | E5   :‖

Repeat ad lib. to fade

Ride The Lightning

Words & Music by
James Hetfield, Lars Ulrich, Cliff Burton & Dave Mustaine

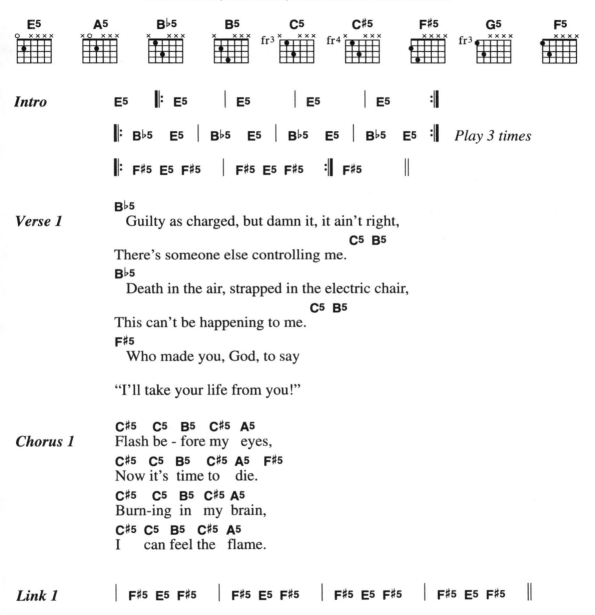

Intro   E5   ‖: E5 | E5 | E5 | E5   :‖

‖: B♭5 E5 | B♭5 E5 | B♭5 E5 | B♭5 E5 :‖   *Play 3 times*

‖: F#5 E5 F#5 | F#5 E5 F#5 :‖ F#5   ‖

Verse 1

B♭5
  Guilty as charged, but damn it, it ain't right,
                                    C5 B5
There's someone else controlling me.

B♭5
  Death in the air, strapped in the electric chair,
                                    C5 B5
This can't be happening to me.

F#5
  Who made you, God, to say

"I'll take your life from you!"

Chorus 1

C#5   C5   B5   C#5   A5
Flash be - fore my   eyes,

C#5   C5   B5   C#5   A5   F#5
Now it's time to   die.

C#5   C5   B5   C#5   A5
Burn-ing in   my   brain,

C#5   C5   B5   C#5   A5
I   can feel the   flame.

Link 1 | F#5 E5 F#5 | F#5 E5 F#5 | F#5 E5 F#5 | F#5 E5 F#5 ‖

Verse 2

B♭5
Wait for the sign to flick the switch of death,

                    C5 B5
It's the beginning of the end.

B♭5
Sweat, chilling cold, as I watch death unfold,

                  C5 B5
Consciousness my only friend.

F♯5
My fingers grip with fear,

What am I doing here?

Chorus 2   As Chorus 1

Link 2   ‖: E5 | E5 G5 E5 G5 | E5 | E5 G5 E5 G5 :‖

Bridge 1

C5   **B5**
Someone help me,   oh please God help me!

B♭5   **A5**
They're trying to take it all away,

F5   **G5**   **B♭5**   **E5**
I don't want to die.

Link 3   ‖: (E5) | E5 G5 E5 G5 :‖ *Play 3 times*

             | E5 | C5 | C5 | B5 | B5 |

             ‖: E5 | C5 | G5 A5 | A5 :‖

Solo   Ad lib.

Link 4   ‖: E5 | E5 G5 E5 G5 | E5 | E5 G5 E5 G5 :‖

Bridge 2

C5   **B5**
Someone help me,   oh please God help me!

B♭5   **A5**
They're trying to take it all away,

F5   **G5**   **B♭5**   **E5**
I don't want to die.

Link 5   ‖: (E5) | E5 G5 E5 G5 :‖   *Play 3 times*

| E5 | C5 | C5 | C5 | C5 |

‖: B♭5   E5 | B♭5   E5 :‖   *Play 5 times*

| B♭5   E5 | B♭5   E5 B5 | B♭5   ‖

Verse 3

B♭5
   Time moving slow, the minutes seem like hours,
               C5 B5
The final curtain call I see.
B♭5
   How true is this? Just get it over with,
               C5 B5
If this is true just let it be.
F#5
   Wakened by horrid scream,

Freed from this frightening dream.

Chorus 3   As Chorus 1

Link 6 | F#5 E5 F#5 | F#5 E5 F#5 | F#5 E5 F#5 | F#5 E5 F#5 ‖

Outro   ‖: F#5 E5 F#5 | C5 | F#5 E5 F#5 | F5   :‖

‖: F#5 E5 F#5 | C5 | F#5 E5 F#5 | E5   :‖

| E5 | E5   ‖

Until It Sleeps

Words & Music by
James Hetfield & Lars Ulrich

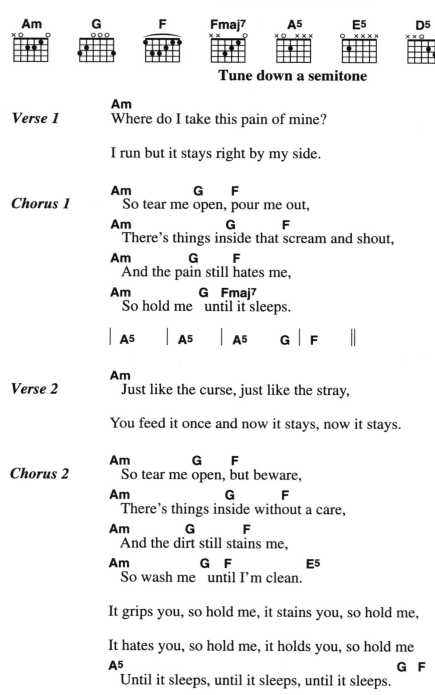

Tune down a semitone

Verse 1

    Am
Where do I take this pain of mine?

I run but it stays right by my side.

Chorus 1

  Am   **G**   **F**
So tear me open, pour me out,

  Am   **G**   **F**
There's things inside that scream and shout,

  Am   **G**   **F**
And the pain still hates me,

  Am   **G** **Fmaj7**
So hold me   until it sleeps.

| **A5** | **A5** | **A5** | **G** | **F** ||

Verse 2

  Am
Just like the curse, just like the stray,

You feed it once and now it stays, now it stays.

Chorus 2

  Am   **G**   **F**
So tear me open, but beware,

  Am   **G**   **F**
There's things inside without a care,

  Am   **G**   **F**
And the dirt still stains me,

  Am   **G** **F**   **E5**
So wash me   until I'm clean.

It grips you, so hold me, it stains you, so hold me,

It hates you, so hold me, it holds you, so hold me
A5   **G** **F**
Until it sleeps, until it sleeps, until it sleeps.

Verse 3

Am
So tell me why you've chosen me,

Don't want your grip, don't want your greed, don't want it.

Chorus 3

Am   **G**   **F**
I'll tear me open, make you gone,
Am   **G**   **F**
No more can you hurt anyone,
Am   **G**   **F**
And the fear still shakes me,
Am   **G** **F**
So hold me   until it sleeps.
E5
It grips you, so hold me, it stains you, so hold me,

It hates you, so hold me, it holds you, holds you, holds you,
A5
Until it sleeps, until it sleeps, until it sleeps,
Am
Until it sleeps, until it sleeps.

| **Am** | **Am** | **Am** | **Am** | **Cmaj7** | **Cmaj7** ‖

Bridge

C
Don't want it.
Cmaj7   **Am**
I don't want it, want it, want it, want it, want it, no.

Chorus 4

Am   **G**   **F**
So tear me open, but beware,
Am   **G**   **F**
There's things inside without a care,
Am   **G**   **F**
And the dirt still stains me,
Am   **G**   **Fmaj7**
So wash me   until I'm clean.
A5   **D5**   **F**
I'll tear me open, make you gone,
A5   **D5**   **F5**
No longer will you hurt anyone,
A5   **D5**   **F**
And the hate still shapes me,
A5   **D5** **F**
So hold me   until it sleeps,
A5
Until it sleeps, until it sleeps,

Until it sleeps, until it sleeps.

The Unforgiven

Words & Music by
James Hetfield, Lars Ulrich & Kirk Hammett

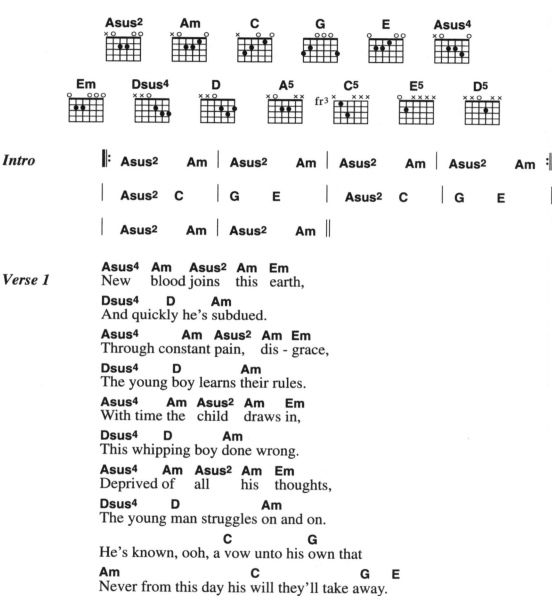

Intro

‖: Asus2   Am │ Asus2   Am │ Asus2   Am │ Asus2   Am :‖

│ Asus2   C │ G   E │ Asus2   C │ G   E │

│ Asus2   Am │ Asus2   Am ‖

Verse 1

Asus4 Am Asus2 Am Em
New   blood joins this   earth,

Dsus4   D   Am
And quickly he's subdued.

Asus4   Am Asus2 Am Em
Through constant pain, dis - grace,

Dsus4   D   Am
The young boy learns their rules.

Asus4   Am Asus2 Am Em
With time the child   draws in,

Dsus4   D   Am
This whipping boy done wrong.

Asus4   Am Asus2 Am Em
Deprived of   all   his   thoughts,

Dsus4   D   Am
The young man struggles on and on.

                    C   G
He's known, ooh, a vow unto his own that

Am   C   G   E
Never from this day his will they'll take away.

Chorus 1

```
                Am                        G
           What I've felt and what I've known,
                    Em                         Am
           Never shined through in what I've shown.
                    C        G
           Never be, never see,
                    E                    Am
           Won't see what might have been.
                       C           G
           What I've felt, what I've known,
                    Em                         Am
           Never shined through in what I've shown.
                    C        G
           Never free, never me,
                    E               Asus²
           So I dub thee unforgiven.

           | (Asus²)     Am | Asus²     Am ||
```

Verse 2

```
           Asus⁴      Am Asus²   Am Em
           They ded - i - cate     their lives
           Dsus⁴ D       Am
           To run-ning all of his,
           Asus⁴   Am Asus²  Am  Em
           He tries to    please them all,
           Dsus⁴  D       Am
           This bit-ter man he is.
           Asus⁴      Am  Asus² Am  Em
           Throughout his   life     the   same,
           Dsus⁴  D            Am
           He's battled constantly,
           Asus⁴    Am Asus²  Am  Em
           This fight he   can - not   win,
           Dsus⁴  D          Am
           A    tired man, they see, no longer cares.
                   C           G         Am
           The old man then prepares to die regretfully,
                   C              G   E
           That old man here is me.
```

Chorus 2   As Chorus 1

Instrumental ||: Asus²   Am | Asus²   Am | Asus²   Am :||

Solo   ‖: A5 | E5 | D5 | A5 :‖ *Play 4 times*

| C G | A5 | C G | E5 ‖

Chorus 3

Am   G
What I've felt and what I've known,

       Em   Am
Never shined through in what I've shown.

          C   G
Never be, never see,

          E   Am
Won't see what might have been.

            C   G
What I've felt, what I've known,

       Em   Am
Never shined through in what I've shown.

        C   G
Never free, never me,

        E   Am
So I dub thee unforgiven.

Outro | (Am) C | G Em | Am C | G E ‖

‖: Am   C   G
    Never free, never me,

        E   Am   C G E
So I dub thee unforgiven,

Am   C   G
    You labelled me, I'll label you,

        E   Am   C G E
So I dub thee unforgiven. :‖ *Repeat to fade*

Welcome Home (Sanitarium)

Words & Music by
James Hetfield, Lars Ulrich & Kirk Hammett

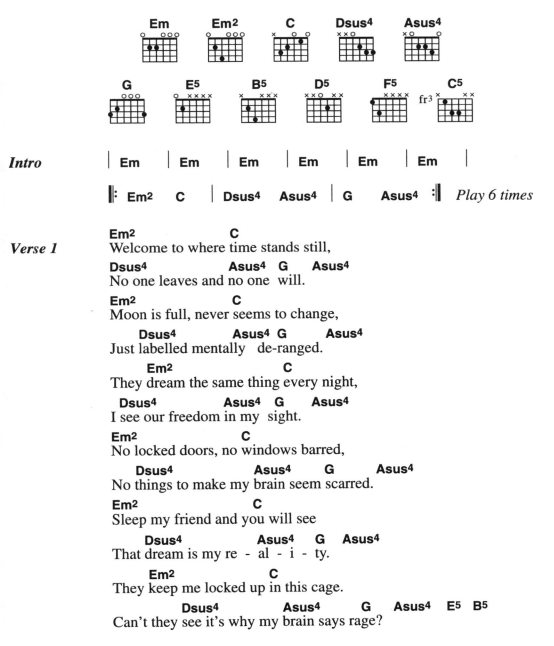

Intro

| Em | Em | Em | Em | Em | Em |

‖: Em² C | Dsus⁴ Asus⁴ | G Asus⁴ :‖ *Play 6 times*

Verse 1

Em²   C
Welcome to where time stands still,

Dsus⁴   Asus⁴ G   Asus⁴
No one leaves and no one will.

Em²   C
Moon is full, never seems to change,

    Dsus⁴   Asus⁴ G   Asus⁴
Just labelled mentally   de-ranged.

        Em²   C
They dream the same thing every night,

    Dsus⁴   Asus⁴ G   Asus⁴
I see our freedom in my sight.

Em²   C
No locked doors, no windows barred,

    Dsus⁴   Asus⁴   G   Asus⁴
No things to make my brain seem scarred.

Em²   C
Sleep my friend and you will see

    Dsus⁴   Asus⁴   G   Asus⁴
That dream is my re - al - i - ty.

        Em²   C
They keep me locked up in this cage.

        Dsus⁴   Asus⁴   G   Asus⁴ E⁵ B⁵
Can't they see it's why my brain says rage?

Chorus 1

B5 E5   B5   E5 B5
Sanitarium,   leave me be,

          E5   B5
Sanitarium,   just leave me alone.

Solo   ‖: Em2   C | Dsus4   Asus4 | G   Asus4 :‖ *Play 4 times*

Verse 2

Em2   C
Build my fear of what's out there,

Dsus4   Asus4 G   Asus4
Cannot breath the open   air.

Em2   C
Whisper things into my brain,

  Dsus4   Asus4 G   Asus4
Assuring me that I'm   in-sane.

       Em2   C
They think our heads are in our hands,

   Dsus4   Asus4 G   Asus4
But violent use brings violent plans.

Em2   C
Keep him tied, it makes him well,

    Dsus4   Asus4   G   Asus4
He's getting better can't you tell?

Em2   C
No more can they keep us in,

Dsus4   Asus4 G   Asus4
Listen, damn it, we will win.

       Em2   C
They see it right, they see it well,

         Dsus4   Asus4   G   Asus4 E5 B5
But they think this saves us from our hell.

Chorus 2

B5 E5   B5   E5
Sanitarium,   leave me be,

B5 E5   B5   E5
Sanitarium,   just leave me alone,

B5   E5
Sanitarium,   just leave me alone.

Instrumental   ‖: E5 | E5 | E5 | E5   :‖   *Play 5 times*

Outro
E5   D5
Fear of living on,
                          F5
Natives getting restless now,
                          C5 B5
Mutiny in the air.
                          E5
Got some death to do.
                          D5
Mirror stares back hard.
                          F5
"Kill", it's such a friendly word.
                          C5   B5   E5
Seems the only way   for reaching out again.

Solo   E5 ad lib.

Whiplash

Words & Music by
James Hetfield & Lars Ulrich

E5	G5	C5	B5	A5	F#5	A♭5

Intro

E5 ad lib.

Verse 1

E5
Late at night, all systems go,

You've come to see the show.
G5 E5
We do our best, you're the rest,

                 G5
You make it real, you know.
E5
There's a feeling deep inside

That drives you fuckin' mad,
G5 E5
A feeling of a hammerhead,

            G5 C5 B5
You need it oh so bad.

Chorus 1

A5 F#5   C5 B5
A - drenaline starts to flow,
A5   F#5   C5 B5 A5
You're thrashing all around,
F#5
Acting like a maniac,
N.C.
Whiplash!

Link 1

‖: E5 | E5 A5 A♭5 G5 | E5 | E5 A5 A♭5 G5 :‖

Verse 2

E5
Bang your head against the stage
                                    G5
Like you never did before.

E5
Make it ring, make it bleed,
                                    G5
Make it really sore.

E5
In a frenzied madness

                                            G5
With your leather and your spikes,

E5
Heads are bobbing around,
                                    G5 C5 B5
It's hot as hell tonight.

Chorus 2   As Chorus 1

Link 2   ‖: E5 | E5 A5 A♭5 G5 | E5 | E5 A5 A♭5 G5 :‖

Verse 3

E5
Here on stage the Marshall noise
                                    G5
Is piercing through your ears.

E5
It kicks your ass, kicks your face,
                                    G5
Exploding feeling nears.

E5
Now's the time to let it rip,

To let it fuckin' loose.

G5   E5
We're gathered here to maim and kill,
                                        G5 C5 B5
'Cause this is what we choose.

Chorus 3   As Chorus 1

Interlude   ‖: E5 | E5 | E5 | E5   :‖   'Here we go…'

Solo ‖: E5 | E5 | E5 | E5 :‖ *Play 4 times*

| Em | N.C. |

Whiplash!

‖: E5 | E5 A5 A♭5 G5 | E5 | E5 A5 A♭5 G5 :‖

Verse 4

E5
Show is through, the metal's gone,

       G5
It's time to hit the road,

E5
Another town, another gig,

       G5
Again we will explode.

E5
Hotel rooms and motorways,

Life out here is raw

G5   E5
But we'll never stop, we'll never quit,

        G5 C5 B5
'Cause we're Metallica.

Chorus 4

A5 F♯5   C5 B5
A - drenaline starts to flow,

A5   F♯5   C5 B5 A5
You're thrashing all around,

F♯5   C5 B5 A5
Acting like a maniac.

Outro

| E5 F♯5 E5 F♯5 E5 | E5 F♯5 E5 F♯5 E5 | E5 F♯5 E5 F♯5 E5 |

| (E5) | E5 F♯5 E5 F♯5 ‖

6/99 (34449)